GLORIOUS WRESTLING ALLIANCE
ULTIMATE CHAMPIONSHIP EDITION

ABOUT THE AUTHOR

Josh Hicks is a cartoonist from South Wales. He was born there in 1991 and has no plans to leave. He currently lives in Cardiff with his partner and their cat. He has yet to wrestle professionally.

ACKNOWLEDGMENTS

Dedicated to Rachel. Special thanks to Ioan Morris, my family, and anyone who helped support or make this book in any way.

Story and art by Josh Hicks

First American edition published in 2021 by Graphic Universe™

Copyright © 2019 by Josh Hicks

Graphic Universe™ is a trademark of Lerner Publishing Group, Inc.

GLORIOUS WRESTLING ALLIANCE
ULTIMATE CHAMPIONSHIP EDITION

JOSH HICKS

GRAPHIC UNIVERSE™ · MINNEAPOLIS

CHAPTER ONE

ONE NIGHT ONLY

9

13

AUDERE EST FACERE, DEAR LISTENERS. WELCOME AGAIN TO THE POET'S CORNER PODCAST.

WITH ME TODAY IS PROFESSIONAL WRESTLER DEATH MACHINE, WHOSE NEW COLLECTION, POEMS BY DEATH MACHINE, IS OUT NOW.

HELLO.

KILL

DEATH MACHINE, THANKS FOR JOINING US.

WOULD YOU CARE TO START BY READING ONE OF YOUR NEW PIECES?

CERTAINLY.

AHEM.

THERE LIES A CEASELESS LONGING, DEEP WITHIN MY SOUL / GRIPPING TIGHT MY BODY, LIKE AN ACHILLES TENDON HOLD.

KILL

FRUITLESS I ROAM THE COUNTRY WHERE WE USED TO LIVE / PILEDRIVEN INTO MEMORY, WITH NOTHING LEFT TO GIVE.

SO HEAVY BEATS MY HEART, AND HEAVY SWAY THE TREES / WILTING LIKE WEIGHT'D TURNBUCKLES, IN THE AUTUMN BREEZE.

WOW.

COME ON, RICKY!

YOU KNOW WE CAN DO IT! LET US FIGHT IN REAL MATCHES! THE WOMAN'S LEAGUE IS A JOKE RIGHT NOW!

I BEG TO DIFFER. LAST WEEK'S PANTIES AND BARBED-WIRE DEATHMATCH WAS VERY WELL RECEIVED.

PFFT. SCREW THAT WEAK, GRATUITOUS NONSENSE!

I MEAN, I COULD TAKE MOST OF THESE ARTIFICIALLY INFLATED MANBABIES WITH MY EYES CLOSED! JUST GIVE ME A CHANCE!

LOOKIN' GOOD, GUURRRL!!

DEATH

LOOK, I'LL CONSIDER IT, ETC. WITH QUOTATION MARKS AROUND "CONSIDER". ANYWAY, I'VE GOT SOME URGENT BUSINESS TO ATTEND TO.

IT'S DRUGS! THE URGENT BUSINESS IS DRUGS! CHAT LATER, YEAH?

GRR

THIS IS RIDICULOUS!!

>SIGH<

FINE.

IF YOU CAN'T BEAT 'EM, JOIN 'EM... AND THEN BEAT 'EM TO DEATH!

RUSTLE

RUSTLE

THEY'LL NEVER KNOW...

snort

WOO!

Sniff

WELL, POP, YOU KNOW WHAT TOMORROW NIGHT IS? IT'S THE NIGHT OF THE ULTRABRAWL.

YOUR BOY'S GONNA MAKE YOU PROUD.

SON, I GOT SOMETHIN' IMPORTANT TO SAY TO YOU.

23

PHEW.

THANK GOD.

BRING THE ACTION HOME WITH
GWA 20XX ™

FEATURING:

RELIVE CLASSIC GWA MOMENTS LIKE NEVER BEFORE!

> THERE LIES A CEASELESS LONGING, DEEP WITHIN MY SOUL

HUNDREDS OF SPECIAL MOVES AND SIGNATURE TAUNTS!

UNLIMITED CREATE-A-WRESTLER OPTIONS!

GROUNDBREAKING CAREER MODE!

> YOU'VE GOT HEALTH INSURANCE, RIGHT?

 1-4 PLAYERS

INTERNET CONNECTION REQUIRED

CHAPTER TWO
GRAPPLING ROAD

COOL? EVERYONE THINKS THE BUS IS COOL AT FIRST. OOH, IT'S *EXCITING*, OOH, IT'LL BE *FUN*, OOH, IT'S A NEAT *FRAMING DEVICE*.

BUT MARK MY WORDS: THIS ROAD IS PAVED WITH CRUSHED SOULS. *WE ARE ALL DOOMED.*

ROSTER MORALE

GREAT CARP
COMPANY ACE

GRAVY TRAIN
ODDLY SHAPED

DEATH MACHINE
TORTURED POET

ERIC PUMMEL
PUNCHMASTER

HORACE KAISER
CHILD OF SATAN

MASK DE CHICKEN
POULTRY GIMMICK

MICHAEL MORRIS III
ENJOYS NAPS, MEATS

MIRANDA FURY
RAGE QUEEN

J. CAROL OUCH
HEAD KICKIST

MASSIVE ROY
BIG MAN

?
(NO DATA AVAILABLE)

HYPER MASK
TRAVELING SEPARATELY

I LOVE HIM! I EVEN MADE THIS *CUSTOM ACTION FIGURE* IN HIS IMAGE!

IT'S GOT HIS NEW OUTFIT AND EVERYTHING!

COOL.

INITIALLY COMPELLED TO DON HER MASKED GUISE BY THE COMPANY'S *ARCHAIC GENDER-BASED BOOKING POLICIES*, MIRANDA NOW FINDS HERSELF *CONFLICTED* IN REGARDS TO HER CREATION.

DOES SHE FEEL *PRIDE* IN HER ACCOMPLISHMENTS? *SHAME* IN HER SECRECY? *JEALOUSY* OF HER OWN ALTER-EGO'S SUCCESSES? MIRANDA CAN'T TELL.

ALL SHE KNOWS FOR SURE IS THE ANXIETY. HOW THE WEIGHT OF HER SECRET BEARS DOWN ON HER ALWAYS; HOW IT CRUSHES HER SLOWLY, LIKE SO MUCH *RUBBLE*.

CHOMP CHOMP CHOMP

SHE ALSO CAN'T HELP THINKING ABOUT HOW THE ARM DETAIL ON THAT ACTION FIGURE ISN'T QUITE RIGHT.

PROGRESS REPORT

"THE JUGGERNAUT"
MULTI-PURPOSE
TOUR VEHICLE
(TEN YEARS
IN STORAGE)

CREW TRAILER
COMPLIANT
WITH MOST HUMAN
RIGHTS STANDARDS

TALENT CABINS
FULLY FURNISHED

FAN PLOW
NON-LETHAL

DAY 19

438 HOURS OF ROAD

ROSTER MORALE

MICHAEL MORRIS III
DEDICATED CARNIVORE

GRAVY TRAIN
FULL OF SAUCE

HORACE KAISER
HORNED DEMON

GREAT CARP
TITLE HOLDER

ROUTE

40

41

DAY 20
453 HOURS OF ROAD

ROSTER MORALE

MICHAEL MORRIS III
HAVING A PLEASANT TIME

GRAVY TRAIN
75% ALCOHOL

HORACE KAISER
SLAVE TO THE RHYTHM

GREAT CARP
GENTLY SOBBING

CARPRADIO ♫

MASSACRE 7
TOP SECRET EPISODE
GENRE: STAB ROCK

1 ALL-OUT ASSAULT
2 36-HOUR SLUGFEST
3 ROOFTOP FRENZY B
4 EVERYTHING GOES WRONG
5 INFERNAL BLEEDING
6 FINAL ASSIGNMENT
7 SEX & FURY
8 MY HEART IS YOURS (COVER)

IT'S *DEPRESSING!* ONE DATE LEFT ON THE TOUR, AND ALL I'VE BEEN GIVEN ARE THESE CRAPPY LITTLE FILLER MATCHES!

ALL I WANT IS ONE SHOT TO TAKE THE BULL BY THE HORNS. AND THEN VIOLENTLY DRIVE IT INTO THE GROUND AND *KICK IT.*

I MEAN, COME ON. I AM *SO MUCH MORE* THAN A FUNNY SILHOUETTE.

THAT'S COOL. I'VE GOT SOMETHING TO SAY NOW, SO PLEASE STOP TALKING.

I'VE GOT A SECRET, AND I NEED TO TELL SOMEONE OR I THINK I'M JUST GOING TO *IMPLODE.* YOU'RE TRUSTWORTHY, RIGHT? WE'VE GOT A BOND.

HEY, GRAVY'S THICKER THAN WATER. AND BLOOD.

I'VE BEEN *LIVING A LIE.* IT'S GOTTEN WAYYY OUT OF HAND, AND GOD... IT'S GOING TO BE SO *GOOD* TO FINALLY GET THIS OFF MY CHEST. I —

WHAT WAS THAT?!

48

RELIVE THE GLORY WITH FULLY ARTICULATED
GWA ACTION FIGURES™

NEW!

**UNBEATABLE STRENGTH!
ULTIMATE POWER!
HIGH-QUALITY PLASTIC!**

GWA RING AND BACKSTAGE BICKERING
AREA PLAYSETS SOLD SEPARATELY!!

ACCESSORIES ALSO AVAILABLE!!

OFFICIAL
GWA
PRODUCT

CHAPTER THREE

GLORIOUS WRESTLING APOCALYPSE

I'M DONE. I'M OUT OF OPTIONS. NOTHING WE DO IS GOING TO PULL US OUT OF THIS HOLE.

RICKY LOVETT JR.
ACTING CEO

-204.607

CAN'T WE JUST DELETE THIS GODDAMN INFOSHEET? KNOWING HOW SCREWED I AM DOWN TO ONE DECIMAL PLACE IS BAD ENOUGH – I DON'T NEED THREE.

YOU CANNOT SIMPLY SEND YOUR FAILURES TO THE RECYCLE BIN, LOVETT.

I JUST WANNA SAY: YOU'RE LIKE, LITERALLY KILLING DAD.

EL FINANCIERO
ÁNGEL INVESTOR

VICKY LOVETT
CHIEF OF PUBLIC RELATIONS

I MEAN, I'M SURE THERE ARE SOME OTHER CONTRIBUTING FACTORS OR WHATEVER, BUT IT CAN'T HELP.

RICKY LOVETT SR.
FORMER CEO,
BOARDMEMBER
(ADVISORY CAPACITY)

THERE HAS TO BE SOMETHING ON THERE WE CAN CUT DOWN ON. WHAT ABOUT 'DRUGS & MISC.'?

TRUST ME, I'VE GOTTEN THAT AS LOW AS IT'LL GO.

DON'T EVEN TALK TO ME ABOUT THE 'MISC.'

GLORIOUS WRESTLING APOCALYPSE

THIS DOCUMENT CHARTS A MOMENT IN TIME THAT IS POPULARLY DUBBED THE MOST **TURBULENT IN GWA HISTORY.** THOUGH THIS STANDPOINT IS SOMEWHAT VALID, IT IS THE OPINION OF THIS AUTHOR THAT THOSE THAT HOLD THIS VIEW WOULD DO WELL TO REMEMBER THE **ARMED UPRISING** THAT TOOK PLACE ONLY THREE DECADES PRIOR, AS WELL AS THE EVENTS OF '**BLACK TUESDAY**' — A FREAK INCIDENT SO COMPLEX AND BAFFLING THAT NO MERE GRAPH OR DIAGRAM WOULD BEGIN TO DO IT JUSTICE.

REGARDLESS, THIS PERIOD SERVED AS A CATALYST FOR GREAT CHANGE WITHIN THE ORGANIZATION, AND IS NOT WITHOUT NOTE. IT ALSO CONVENIENTLY LENDS ITSELF TO BOTH THE TIMELINE AND 24-PAGE COMIC MEDIUMS, SO: HAPPY READING!!

1   2   3

▶▶ TIMELINE OF EVENTS

OR THE FALL OF THE GLORIOUS WRESTLING ALLIANCE
(AN HISTORICAL ACCOUNT IN COMICS FORM)

KEY PLAYERS   IN NO PARTICULAR ORDER

GREAT CARP	HYPER MASK	MIRANDA FURY
COMPANY ACE, REIGNING CHAMPION, FISH HEAD.	MYSTERIOUS MASKED SUPERSTAR.	STAR OF WOMEN'S DIVISION. SECRETLY HYPER MASK!
DEATH MACHINE	GRAVY TRAIN	RICKY LOVETT JR.
WILD BEAST, FRUSTRATED POET.	LITERALLY MADE OF GRAVY.	UNDER-QUALIFIED CEO. PANICKED.

1- BUSINESS AS USUAL; 2 - OPPORTUNITIES IN MERCHANDISING; 3 - THE ART LIFE;
4 - NEW GIMMICK, SAME GRAVY TRAIN; 5 - MASKED NO MORE;
6 - A FUTILE GAMBIT; 7 - APOCALYPSE

GREAT CARP, GRAYSON TAINT AND ELLEN FISHER. ELLEN AND GRAYSON, GREAT CARP.

IT'S AN HONOR.

WE'RE ALL REALLY EXCITED AT THE PROSPECT OF WORKING TOGETHER. I'M TELLING YOU: *CARP VODKA* IS JUST THE *TIP OF THE ICEBERG!*

NOW, I'M A *HUGE FAN.* NOT OF PROFESSIONAL WRESTLING, OBVIOUSLY– I'M A 42 YEAR-OLD MAN – BUT OF THE *GREAT CARP BRAND!* YOU'VE GOT WHAT WE CALL *H.M.P* – HUGE MERCHANDISING POTENCH.

THAT'S INDUSTRY LINGO FOR POTENTIAL, BTW.

YOU'VE GOT IT ALL — GRAVITAS, CHARISMA, AND A HEAD THAT CAN BE EASILY REPLICATED USING INJECTION MOLDING! *THE TRIFECTA!*

TAKE A LOOK AT SOME OF THE PROTOTYPES WE'VE BEEN KICKING AROUND.

ALARM CLOCK
ADVANCED SNOOZE FUNCTION

11:15

TOILET PLUNGER
DESIGNED FOR HIGH-PROTEIN DIETS

CARP WASH

ORAL HYGIENE KIT
9/10 DENTISTS RECOMMEND

WHAT DO YOU THINK? *GREAT STUFF,* HUH?

YOUR *HEAD* IS GONNA MAKE US ALL *RICH!*

THIS PERIOD OF GWA HISTORY PROVED PIVOTAL FOR ALL OF THE ROSTER — NOT LEAST DEATH MACHINE.

THOUGH A RESPECTED AND FEROCIOUS COMPETITOR IN HIS OWN RIGHT, DEATH MACHINE'S BUDDING POETRY CAREER WOULD AT THIS POINT BEGIN TO OCCUPY MOST, IF NOT ALL, OF HIS THOUGHTS.

IT IS ENTIRELY POSSIBLE THAT THESE OUTSIDE CONCERNS HAD SOME IMPACT ON HIS IN-RING PERFORMANCE.

WHAT RHYMES WITH GRAPEFRUIT?

TAKE ROOT. ESCAPE ROUTE. QUAALUDE?

SLAM

THE ARTIST ALSO CONTINUED TO SELL HIS WORK AT SHOWS AND FAIRS COUNTRY-WIDE.

ANY EVIDENCE SUPPORTING DEATH MACHINE'S REPEATED CLAIM THAT HE 'BROKE EVEN' AT SUCH EVENTS HAS YET TO SURFACE.

ECHOES OF THESE EXPERIENCES CAN BE DETECTED IN HIS EIGHTH SELF-PUBLISHED VOLUME, 'DREAMS UNSOLD'.

DREAMS UNSOLD

POEMS BY DEATH MACHINE

DREAMS UNSOLD WOULD ULTIMATELY GO ON TO SELL 16 COPIES (PRINT RUN: 250).

D.M.'S WORK ALSO WENT UNRECOGNIZED WITHIN HIS NEW PEER GROUP.

IT'S NICE HOW YOU'RE HAPPY WRITING SO *SIMPLY*. I'D NEVER HAVE THE CONFIDENCE TO DO THAT IN MY WORK.

WHAT A *DICK!*

... BUT HE'S SO *COOL*.

HEY! DEATH MACHINE! COULD WE GET A QUICK PHOTO?

NOT NOW, GUYS. I'VE GOTTA, UH ...

..., WELL, I JUST DON'T WANT TO, AND I CAN'T THINK OF A FAKE EXCUSE. SORRY.

HE JUST TREATED US LIKE *GARBAGE!*

I KNOW!

HE'S SO *COOL!*

GOTTA SAY, *GRAVY TRAIN*: YOU'VE REALLY TAKEN A SHINE TO THIS NEW *BAD-BOY PERSONA.*

I KNOW! ONE DAY I JUST REALIZED: *LOATHING* IS PRACTICALLY THE SAME AS *LOVE* — AND IT'S EASIER TO GET! CHECK OUT MY *FANMAIL!*

🏠 **MENTIONS** ☰

@grappledog6
@gravytrain omg u r insufferable trash

@mrcalm
@gravytrain ▓▓▓ u i hope u ▓▓▓▓▓ ▓▓ and ▓▓▓▓▓▓▓▓▓▓ u pig

@massive_roy_wrestler
@gravytrain dude there's gravy all over the locker room again, come on

AAAAHHHHH... SWEET, SWEET ACKNOWLEDGMENT.

NOURISHING HATE FUMES

I EVEN GOT MYSELF A BRAND-NEW EVIL MOVESET!

① ②

PFDOOSH!

SIGNATURE MOVE
BROWN MIST

MIRANDA FURY
MID-CARD STALWART

HT: 5'4"; WT: 149 lbs

FINISHING MOVE:
FURIOUS LEG DROP

FAVORITE FOOD:
BOILED EGG (3-4 MINS)

1!2!3!

I WAS ON FIRE TONIGHT! THAT CROWD WAS AT MY FEET. EATIN' OUTTA THE PALM OF MY SWEATY HAND!

AND HEY, YOU WERE OKAY TOO!

GUYS! HYPER MASK IS ON NEXT! WE'RE ALL GONNA HANG OUT AND WATCH FROM THE BACK! YOU IN?

ER, I'M GOOD. I'M GONNA SHOWER. FOR LIKE THE ENTIRE MATCH, PROBABLY.

PFT, SHOWER. I'D BE SHOWERING IN YOUR TEARS IF YOU KNEW HYPER MASK'S TRUE IDENTITY, LOSERS.

"OOH, I'M THE BEST. HERE - HAVE SOME UNSOLICITED FEEDBACK. HERE'S A CLUMSY MIXED METAPHOR TO GO WITH IT."

MASSACRE 7

SICK OF IT!

76

MAN, I CAN'T BELIEVE MIRANDA'S BEEN *HYPER MASK* THIS WHOLE TIME. SHE'S *AMAZING!*

I SWEAR I TOLD YOU ALL, LIKE, *MONTHS* AGO.

I'M SORRY, MAN, I DIDN'T PAY ATTENTION.

I THINK I JUST ASSUMED YOU WERE HAVING ONE OF YOUR *MOMENTS.*

HEY! WRESTLERS! STOP *CHATTING!* WE'VE GOT A *CRISIS!*

CARP HAS, UH, *GONE OFF* – SO WE NEED SOMEONE TO FILL HIS PLACE IN THE MAIN EVENT! WHERE'S *DEATH MACHINE* RIGHT NOW?!

AT THAT MOMENT, DEATH MACHINE WAS ENJOYING AN EVENING OF *LEISURE.*

JUST FORTY MORE COPIES TO FOLD AND STAPLE.

SOMEBODY ASSASSINATE ME.

MUCH OF THE WORK ASSEMBLED OVER THE COURSE OF THIS EVENING WOULD LATER COMPRISE THE BACKBONE OF DEATH MACHINE'S EVENTUAL *BREAKOUT COLLECTION.*

THE SOUL, BARED

DEATH MACHINE

JUST $12.99*

* FIRST 100 ORDERS INCLUDE SIGNED BOOKPLATE!

FACING LIMITED OPTIONS, LOVETT WAS FORCED TO STOOP TO UNPRECEDENTED LOWS.

GRAVY TRAIN HEADLINING A MAIN EVENT... DAD MUST BE SPINNING IN HIS *12ft METAL LIFE-SUPPORT UNIT.*

IS THAT MIRANDA?

MY OFFICE, NOW.

LEAVE IT, LOVETT. I JUST MADE YOU MORE POTENTIAL CASH IN ONE NIGHT THAN YOU'VE MADE IN *YEARS.*

CHAPTER 3
GET PAID

I'LL SEE YOU ON MONDAY.

○ ○ ○

NOBODY KNOWS WHEN EXACTLY LOVETT KNEW THAT HIS DAYS AT THE HEAD OF THE GWA WERE NUMBERED. MANY HAVE CITED **THIS EXCHANGE AS THE TURNING POINT...**

... WHILE OTHERS HAVE SUGGESTED THAT IT WAS THE RECEIPT OF A HEFTY MEDICAL BILL *FOR IN-RING GRAVY BURNS.*

TSSST

ARGGHH! I CAN SMELL MY OWN *SKIN!*

WHILE FIRST EDITION COPIES OF DEATH MACHINE'S EVENTUAL OPUS WOULD SEE **STAGGERING** RESALE PRICES...

THE SOUL, BARED

DEATH MACHINE

DEATH MACHINE THE SOUL BARED FIRST-EDITION HARDCOVER

$325 4 BIDS

CONDITION: MINT
👀 12 WATCHING

PLACE BID

... THEY WOULD BE DWARFED BY THE SUMS FETCHED BY A DAMAGED, ONE OF A KIND **CARPCO.** PROTOTYPE.

GREAT CARP RICE COOKER MICRO XTREMELY RARE CARPCO PRODUCT

$14,000 16 BIDS

CONDITION: ACCEPTABLE
👀 3,378 WATCHING

PLACE BID

AARRGHH!!

STUPID, DUMB HEAD,...

I JUST QUIT THE *ONLY* THING I CARE ABOUT...

AND I DON'T EVEN FEEL *BAD* ABOUT IT.

DO I FEEL BAD ABOUT HOW I DON'T FEEL BAD?

LIFE TRULY IS A TRIP.

AND THOUGH, IN ITS OWN WAY, CARP'S STORY WOULD ULTIMATELY BE A TRIUMPHANT ONE...

MAYBE I SHOULD START THERAPY. I'VE GOT THE FREE TIME NOW.

I'LL WORK ON MYSELF. I'LL BE A BETTER CARP.

HAPPIER, CALMER, LESS QUICK TO RAGE.

... HE WOULD FIRST NEED TO GO THROUGH SOME DARK NIGHTS OF THE SOUL.

WHO'S LEAVING ALL THESE BEER CANS LYING AROUND!?

KICK

STATUS UPDATE

GREAT CARP	HYPER FURY	N/A
PROFESSIONALLY A.W.O.L.	SUPERSTAR IN OWN RIGHT.	N/A
DEATH MACHINE	GRAVY TRAIN	RICKY LOVETT JR.
AWAITING GREATNESS.	MADE THE BIG TIME (BY DEFAULT.)	LOOKING FOR WORK.

MORE LIKE THIS

"MISADVENTURES IN PLUMBING"

"BEACH EPISODE"

"RESURRECTION"

"THE EARTH MUST SPIN AND CANNOT STOP.
THE SHOW MUST GO ON, NO MATTER WHAT.
AND THOUGH ALL IS NEVER FULLY LOST,
WE MUST ALL ENDURE OUR ELBOW DROPS."

– DEATH MACHINE
'MOTIVATIONAL POEM 8'
FROM 'THE SOUL, BARED'
20XX

CHAPTER FOUR

THE BALLAD OF GREAT CARP

CHANGE IS A CONSTANT, THAT MUCH WE ALL KNOW.

WE MUST MOVE WITH THE EBB AND MUST MOVE WITH THE FLOW.

THIS CHANGE CAN BE FRIEND, CAN BE FOE, CAN BE NEITHER,

CAN SHATTER YOUR BONES, LIKE A DEATH VALLEY DRIVER.

HOW WE COPE WITH THIS CHANGE DEPENDS ON STRENGTH AND ON WILL.

OR, IN THIS CASE, ON FIN AND ON GILL.

NOW PLAYING > **DEATH MACHINE'S POETRY CORNER**
THE BALLAD OF GREAT CARP

YOU MIGHT ALSO LIKE:

HYPER FURY VS MASSIVE ROY at FIGHT PARADE 20XX

ERIC PUMMEL VS GRAVY TRAIN at ROAD TO ULTRA BRAWL XXVI

MICHAEL MORRIS III POST-MATCH CONFERENCE at SLAM GALA VI

ACTIVE ROSTER

HYPER FURY

MASK DE CHICKEN

GRAVY TRAIN

DEATH MACHINE

ERIC PUMMEL

GERTRUDE STEINER

MASSIVE ROY

HORACE KAISER

MICHAEL MORRIS III

JOYCE C. OUCH

SLICK SILVER

HANK LAROUX

LOS BROS HERMANOS

SATAN'S CHILDREN

I'M ABOUT SIXTY PERCENT DECENT.

ARE YOU STILL PLAYING THAT GAME?

YEAH.

EVIDENCE: OF POOR PERSONAL HYGIENE

AT THE MOMENT, I'VE MADE **DEATH MACHINE** THE CHAMPION. HE BETRAYED ME IN A PIVOTAL TAG TEAM MATCH, **DICK**.

I'M CURRENTLY BUILDING UP TO BEAT HIM AND THE REST OF THE EVIL **POETRY-THEMED FACTION** THAT I MADE UP. **EXCITING!!**

ALSO, MY MAIN GUY IS IN THE START OF A BLOSSOMING RELATIONSHIP WITH **GRAVY TRAIN**, WHICH IS PRETTY COOL.

"HEH, THANKS. MAYBE I'LL GIVE YOU A CALL SOMETIME."

I RAN A TOURNAMENT TO SEE WHO'D BE WORTHY OF MY AFFECTIONS, AND HE WON. WE'RE TAKING IT SLOW FOR NOW!

WOW. IT'S COOL THAT THEY PUT ALL THOSE FEATURES IN THERE.

WELL, THEY PUT MOST OF THEM IN. BUT I HAVE MY OWN **PAPER-BASED SYSTEM.** I MADE **DIAGRAMS!!**

CARP WRESTLING ASSOCIATION

THAT SEEMS... FINE? IS THIS *LITERALLY* ALL YOU'VE BEEN DOING SINCE THE LAST TIME I WAS HERE?

FIRST OF ALL, *STRUCTURED PLAY* IS AS IMPORTANT TO THE *GROWN ADULT* AS IT IS TO THE *DEVELOPING CHILD.*

SECONDLY, *NO.* I'VE ALSO BEEN CHARTING A PICTORIAL REPRESENTATION OF MY COMPLEX EMOTIONAL SPECTRUM.

-- HAPPINESS LINE --

N   MON   TUE   WED   THU   FRI   SAT   SU

WITH *MARKERS!*

WHEN DID YOU GO OUTSIDE LAST?

ABOUT FOUR *'NON-PLUSSED'* FACES AGO.

I DREW A LITTLE TREE FOR IT,

ANYWAY, THE MERCHANDISE PEOPLE DON'T LIKE ME GOING OUT IN CASE I DO SOMETHING *'DAMAGING TO THE BRAND,'*

IF I DO GO OUTSIDE, I'M MEANT TO WEAR THE *BIG HEAD.*

IT STINKS IN THERE...

PLACE ON REAL HEAD

WELL, THAT'S SORT OF WHY I CAME HERE.

CUP

CUP

I LOOKED OVER THAT *BIG CONTRACT* YOU SIGNED WITHOUT READING.

WHICH, *BUSINESS TIP,* YOU SHOULD NEVER DO AGAIN —

BUSINESS SIP →

AND WHILE YOU'RE PROHIBITED FROM TAKING ON ANY NEW, *NON-CARPCO* COMMITMENTS, YOU'RE STILL TECHNICALLY ENTITLED TO WORK WITH THE *GWA.*

IF, UH, YOU WANTED TO.

YUCK! NO! THEY DIDN'T APPRECIATE *ME* AND I DON'T NEED *THEM.*

I'M HAPPY HERE, IN MY *GILDED CAGE,* SURROUNDED BY *EXPENSIVE DISTRACTIONS* AND MY *OWN FILTH.*

✕ SKIP

EVEN IF I *DID* WANT TO, I VOWED TO MYSELF TO NEVER WORK WITH LOVETT AGAIN, I NEVER BREAK A CARP VOW!

THAT PERIOD OF MY LIFE IS FINISHED, I'M OVER IT.

GSo   VIDEO GAME

GWA 20XX

EVIDENCE: TO THE CONTRARY

WELL, IF IT MAKES ANY DIFFERENCE, I DON'T THINK LOVETT IS RUNNING THE SHOW OVER THERE ANYMORE.

NOT *THAT* LOVETT, ANYWAY.

YOU'RE GOING TO BE GREAT TONIGHT! YOU'RE A *STAR!*

THANKS, VICKY!

VICKY LOVETT ACTING CEO

HYPER FURY FACE OF THE COMPANY

DID, UH, YOU MANAGE TO FIND ME AN *OPPONENT* FOR ULTRABRAWL?

I MEAN, I LOVE MAKING MASSIVE ROY'S TEETH COME OUT OF HIS NOSE, BUT THERE'S ONLY SO MANY TIMES WE CAN DO THAT BEFORE IT BECOMES *STALE.*

OR HE RUNS OUT OF TEETH.

I'M ON IT! NEW *GWA POLICY* - LISTEN TO THE ROSTER!

IN FACT, I'VE JUST PUT TOGETHER A LIST OF SOME OF THE *BEST FREE AGENTS IN THE WORLD!*

ALL *ITCHING* FOR A SHOT AT THE *CHAMPIONSHIP BELT!*

A CHAMPIONSHIP BELT THAT I *STILL* DON'T PHYSICALLY HAVE...

I KNOW, I KNOW. CARP STILL HAS IT, AND HIS PEOPLE WON'T LET ME THROUGH TO HIM.

WE'RE IN THE PROCESS OF MAKING A NEW ONE AS WE SPEAK. I KNOW IT'S NOT *THE SAME*, BUT IT'S SOMETHING.

ANYWAY, I'VE GOTTA HIT THIS BOARD MEETING. CATCH UP IN A BIT?

PUBLIC FACE
'FRIENDLY, POSITIVE'

OKAY, UH, SEE YOU LATER!

SWITCH!

PRIVATE FACE
'SULLEN, NEGATIVE'

NEW GWA POLICY...

LIE SHAMELESSLY TO THE ROSTER.

SHUT

THANKS FOR AGREEING TO MEET ME OUT HERE.

I KNOW IT'S A *WEIRD SPOT* BUT I'VE GOT TO KIND OF KEEP A LOW PROFILE.

HOPEFULLY PEOPLE WILL JUST THINK I'M A *WAITER ON BREAK.*

THAT'S QUITE ALRIGHT, CARP.

DID YOU BRING MY BELT?

UH – NO, DID YOU GUYS WANT IT BACK? YOU SHOULD HAVE JUST *CALLED.*

DID YOU CALL?

PLEASE JUST SAY WHY YOU BROUGHT US HERE BEFORE ONE OF US *BEATS YOU TO DEATH* WITH A *FOOD TRAY.*

I VOLUNTEER TO DO ALL BEATING.

I WANT TO *COME BACK.*

I REALLY WANT TO COME BACK.

⭐ THE DAILY WRISTLOCK ⭐

NEWS   REVIEWS   DATABASE   BASELESS SPECULATION

HOTTEST NEWS   SORT ▼▲

GREAT CARP PICTURED IN TALKS WITH GWA TOP BRASS – RETURN IMMINENT?

MASSIVE ROY GIVES EXPLOSIVE FOUR-HOUR SHOOT INTERVIEW

CARP PUBLISHING ENDEAVORS TO RELEASE DEATH MACHINE'S 'THE SOUL, BARED'

LAVISH...
OPULENT...

EAU DE CARP

MASSACRE
7
NOW TOURING WORLDWIDE

ULTRA BRAWL XXVI

? VS

TOMORROW
8PM / GWA NET

ULTRABRAWL XXVI

MATCH CARD

RUNTIME: MEDIUM-LONG

I SATAN'S CHILDREN v LOS BROS HERMANOS
DEATH-THEMED OPENING GAMBIT!

II SLICK SILVER v HANK LAROUX
OLD-FASHIONED PUNCH-UP!

III GRAVY TRAIN v MASK DE CHICKEN
GRAVY-AND-FEATHER MATCH!

IV MORRIS & PUMMEL (C) v OUCH & STEINER
TAG-TEAM TITLE SHOWDOWN!

V DEATH MACHINE v MASSIVE ROY
SANCTITY OF THE WRITTEN WORD GRUDGE MATCH!

VI MAIN EVENT: HYPER FURY (C) v ???
A BATTLE TO DECLARE THE ULTIMATE CHAMPION!

GWA ARENAPLEX   DOORS 7:00PM

ATTENDANCE

33,514 / 35,000

HYPE

BACKSTAGE

OKAY. I'M BACK. IT'S GREAT TO SEE YOU ALL. HOPEFULLY AT LEAST SOME OF YOU ARE HAPPY TO SEE ME.

NO NEED TO RESPOND.

I'M GOING TO BE HERE IN A *SLIGHTLY DIFFERENT ROLE* FROM NOW ON.

I'VE COME TO REALIZE THAT THE GWA IS A PART OF ME - AND IF YOU'RE STILL HERE, IT'S A PART OF YOU, TOO.

MAIN EVENT

THE FOLLOWING MAIN EVENT IS SCHEDULED FOR *ONE FALL*, AND IS TO CROWN THE *ULTIMATE GWA HEAVYWEIGHT CHAMPION!*

INTRODUCING FIRST... *HYPER FURY!* AND HER OPPONENT...

GREAT CARP!

BACKSTAGE

TONIGHT IS A *TURNING POINT* FOR THE GWA. SOME PEOPLE WILL SAY IT WAS THE *MONEY* THAT SAVED US. AND THOSE PEOPLE WOULD TECHNICALLY BE 'RIGHT' AND 'CORRECT'...

...BUT I'D SAY IT'S THE *PASSION* THAT SAVED US.

THE *PASSION* THAT EACH AND EVERY ONE OF YOU HAVE FOR THIS WEIRD, *ILLOGICAL* THING.

KILL

MAIN EVENT

DRAG

SLAM

BACKSTAGE

LET'S *USE* THAT PASSION. LET'S GO OUT THERE AND START MAKING THIS THE GWA WE ALWAYS *KNEW* IT COULD BE.

COOL. ANYONE WANT TO GO GET BURRITOS BEFORE THE SHOW?

KILL

I COULD EAT.

MAIN EVENT

SUPLEX

POETRY CORNER

WITH WHAT INTERNAL FIENDS YOU WRESTLE, CARP, WE MAY NEVER BE CERTAIN,

BUT A WARRIOR'S ROLE IS TO FIGHT THE FIGHT UNTIL THAT FINAL CURTAIN.

MAIN EVENT

REVERSAL

ULTRABRAWL XXVI

RESULTS

I — LOS BROS HERMANOS *def.* SATAN'S CHILDREN
11:35, VICTORY BY PINFALL!

II — SLICK SILVER *def.* HANK LAROUX
12:45, VICTORY BY SUBMISSION!

III — GRAVY TRAIN *def.* MASK DE CHICKEN
16:12, VICTORY BY GRAVY-AND-FEATHERING!

IV — OUCH & STEINER (C) *def.* MORRIS & PUMMEL
18:20, TITLE CHANGE BY PINFALL!

V — DEATH MACHINE *def.* MASSIVE ROY
25:35, VICTORY BY SUBMISSION!

VI — MAIN EVENT: HYPER FURY (C) *def.* GREAT CARP (C)
37:30, ULTIMATE TITLE CROWNING BY PINFALL!

EXCITEMENT

ATHLETICISM

STORYTELLING

MERCH SALES

OVERALL RATING: **A+** GJOOBD-

YOU KNOW, THINGS ARE ACTUALLY LOOKING *PRETTY GOOD.*

WE LOST THE GRAVY CHAMBER, BUT I THINK IT'S FOR THE BEST.

MIRANDA'S THE *BEST CHAMP* WE EVER HAD, AND THE NEW CARP MONEY MEANS WE ACTUALLY GET *PAID* PROPERLY!

ALSO, I THINK THEY'RE FIXING THE COFFEE MACHINE!

PLUS, THIS NEW *HEARTTHROB ROLE* I'VE BEEN CAST IN HAS PAID DIVIDENDS. *SEXY DIVIDENDS.*

YOU SHOULD SEE *THESE* DMS!

I EVEN HEARD MORRIS HAS GIVEN UP MEAT.

MY LIFE IS A DARK ABYSS OF PAIN AND TORMENT!

WHAT A GOLDEN ERA FOR US ALL.